More Maths (

Graded problems for 7–10 year-olds

Anne Joshua

STANLEY THORNES

Copyright © Longman Cheshire 1991

First published in 1991 by
Longman Cheshire Pty Limited, Australia

Reprinted in 1994 by Simon & Schuster Education

This edition published exclusively for W H Smith 1997 by
Stanley Thornes (Publishers) Ltd
Ellenborough House
Wellington Street
Cheltenham
GL50 1YW

97 98 99 00 01 \ 10 9 8 7 6 5 4 3 2 1

Designed by Norma van Rees
Illustrations by Boris Silvestri
Set in Plantin Light 12½/14½pt.
Printed in Great Britain by The Baskerville Press, Salisbury, Wiltshire

A catalogue record of this book is available from the British Library

ISBN 0-7487-3402-3

Contents

Introduction

This series of eight books will help to stimulate and challenge your child to think and develop mathematically, enabling them to relate mathematics to everyday life and to think logically and more strategically.

The activities, which all support National Curriculum mathematics and are excellent examples of good practice in mathematics, are graded to allow you to observe and participate in your child's development. The activities are lively and will really get your child thinking.

Here are some practical suggestion on how you can help:

- Ensure your child understands the question.

- Where do I start? Beginning is often a block for children; encourage them, pretend to be a detective and see what clues you have already.

- Encourage your child to have the confidence to have a go.

- In some of the activities there could be several solutions; let your child know that there may be many ways to solve the question.

- Can you find a pattern? Asking your child if he/she can see any common features is a major step in mathematical thinking. Once children begin to see and explore patterns, they gain confidence and are often able to use the information gathered again in a new situation.

- Let's get organised! Encourage your child to put thoughts on paper, firstly so that he/she can make sense of them and, then, so that others are able to understand the notes he/she makes. This is an important aspect of mathematics. This may need some help from you. Show your child how you would set the information out: it will give clues and demonstrate the need to be systematic. Getting organised is one aspect of mathematics which will take time ... it requires patience and understanding.

- Can you find a rule? Many of the activities in the books will encourage your child to find a rule and check whether the rule works in all cases. Encourage your child to reflect on the problem he/she has solved and to discuss what he/she has learnt from it.

- Keep a record of your child's work and look back on the progress he/she has made.

Missing shapes

In each exercise below, the space shows where two shapes must be drawn in order to complete the pattern. Draw the missing shapes.

1 □ ○ □ ○ ○ ○ □ ○ □ ○ _____ ○ □ ○ ○

2 ⬯ □ ⬯ ⬯ □ □ ⬯ □ ⬯ _____

3 ○ ○ ◎ ○ ○ ◎ ○ _____

4 ⬭ □ □ ○ ○ ○ ⬭ _____ ○ ○ ⬭ □ □ ○ ○ ○ ⬭

5 ○ △ ○ ○ ◇ ○ △ _____ ◇ ○ △ ○ ○

6 ▱ ◇ □ ◇ ▱ ◇ _____ ▱ ◇ □ ◇ ▱ ◇

7 ○ △ ○ ○ □ ○ △ ○ ○ _____ △ ○ ○ □ ○ △ ○ ○

8 △ ▯ △ △ △ ▯ △ ▯ △ △ _____ △ ▯ △ △ △

9 M D C D M D _____ M D C D M D C

10 C M C C D C M _____ D C M C C D C M

11 • ∥ • • • \ • ∥ • • _____ • ∥ • • • \ • ∥

12 Make up a 'missing shape' pattern of your own.

Faces

1 Here is a face.
The eyes are open.
The mouth is happy.
The hair is curly.

Now both eyes are open ○ ○
but they could be closed — —

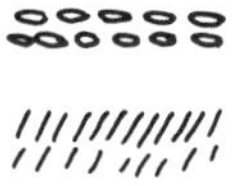

The mouth is happy ⌣
but it could be sad ⌢
or normal —

The hair is curly ∞∞∞∞
but it could be straight ///////////

It is possible to make twelve different faces by combining these features in different ways.
Can you draw them all?   Can you draw any more?

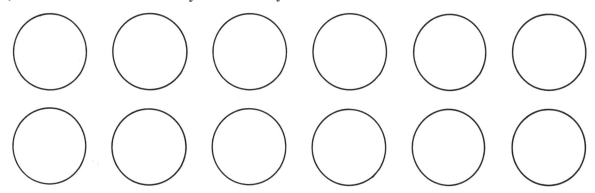

2 The face can be different again.

The eyes can
look straight ahead ◖◗
or look to the right ◐◐
or look to the left ◑◑

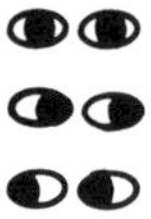

The hair can be
parted in the middle
or brushed back

The mouth can be
happy ⌣
or sad ⌢

How many different faces can you draw this time?
How do you know that you have drawn them all?

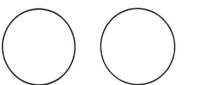

Shapes and symbols

Which shapes or symbols must be added to these squares in order to make the patterns complete? Explain the patterns you see.

1

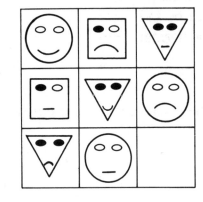

2

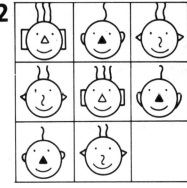

3

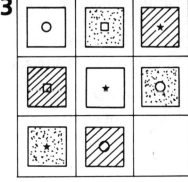

4

5

6

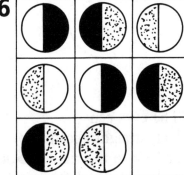

7

8

9

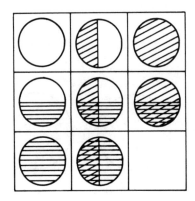

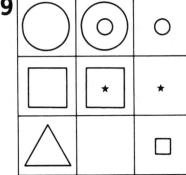

Torn rectangles

Eight rectangles were drawn on squared paper which was then accidentally torn. How many little squares made up each original rectangular shape before it was torn?

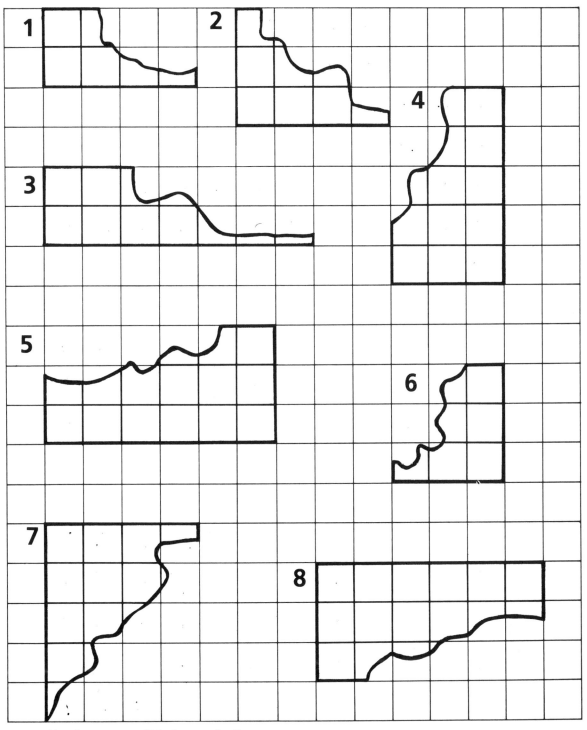

Describe how you did these challenges.

Shape puzzles

To solve these puzzles, first draw dotted lines in the figures, then count the shapes.

1 How many times will ☐ fit into each of these figures?

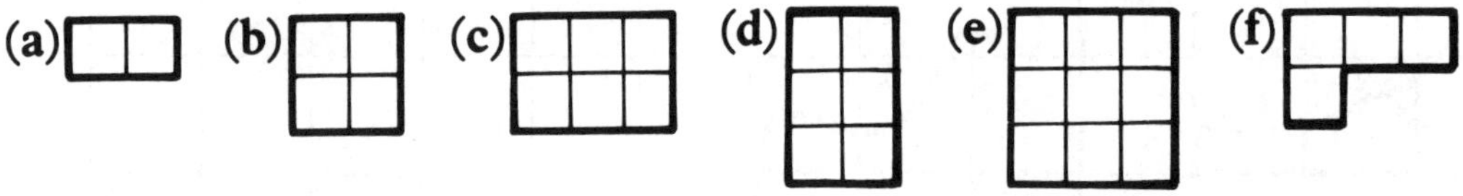

(a) (b) (c) (d) (e) (f)

2 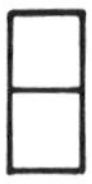 ▯ will fit twice into ⊞ and this can be done in

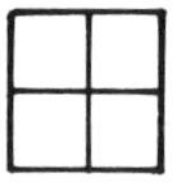

two ways: ▯ or ▭

How many of these  ▯ will fill each of these figures?

(a) (b) (c) (d) (e)

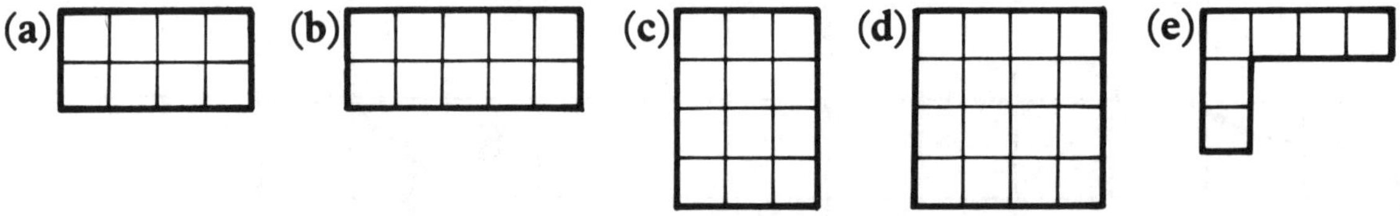

3 How many of these  △ will fill each of these figures?

(a) (b) (c) (d) (e)

(f) (g) (h)

LET'S GET INTO SHAPE!

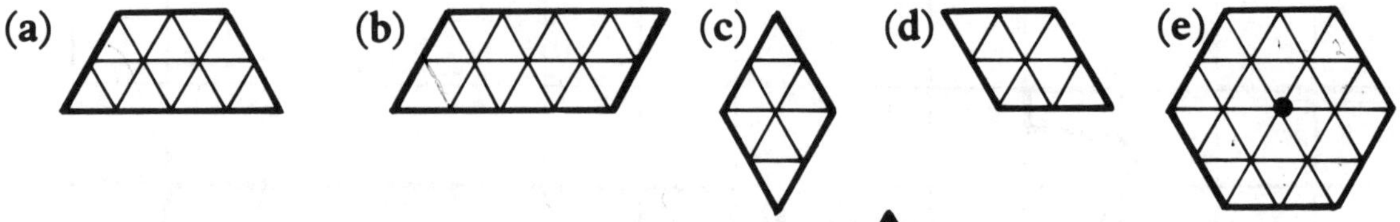

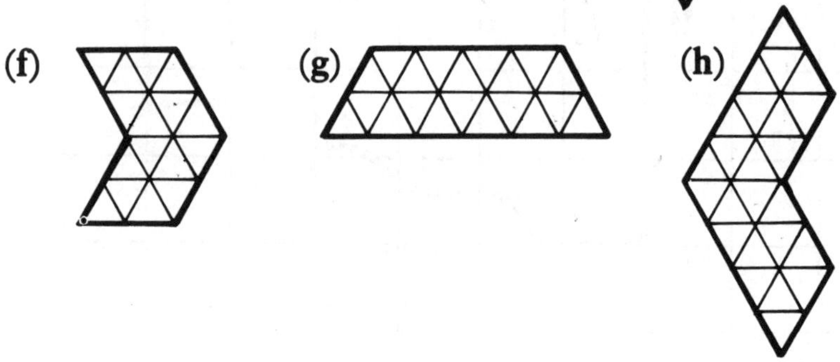

Number sentences

Use any combination of the symbols $+$, $-$ and $\times$ to make the groups of numbers given below into true statements.

For example, if you are given the numbers 1 4 3 = 1, you will need the symbols $\times$ and $-$ to make a number sentence: $(1 \times 4) - 3 = 1$. The brackets show that you do 1×4 first and then subtract 3.

In each sentence you need to put brackets in to show which one to do first.

$1 + \underbrace{(2 \times 3)}_{\text{(first)}} = 1 + 6$ $\qquad$ $\underbrace{(1 + 2)}_{\text{(first)}} \times 3 = 3 \times 3$
$ = 7$ $\qquad\qquad\qquad = 9$

1	1	2	3	=	0
2	1	3	2	=	1
3	1	3	2	=	2
4	2	3	1	=	4
5	2	3	1	=	5
6	1	2	3	=	6
7	1	3	4	=	7
8	2	4	6	=	0
9	2	4	6	=	2
10	2	3	5	=	1
11	2	5	6	=	4
12	2	5	1	=	9
13	2	4	3	=	5
14	6	2	4	=	8
15	2	6	4	=	4
16	2	4	5	=	3
17	2	3	1	=	7
18	2	5	2	=	12
19	2	5	2	=	8
20	2	6	5	=	7

Try and see what happens to some of these sentences when you change the position of the brackets. Discuss this with your teacher.

Shading circles

When a circle is divided into two equal parts (halves), each half is called a semicircle.

1 In this exercise, each semicircle must be either shaded in one of two ways, or , or left blank

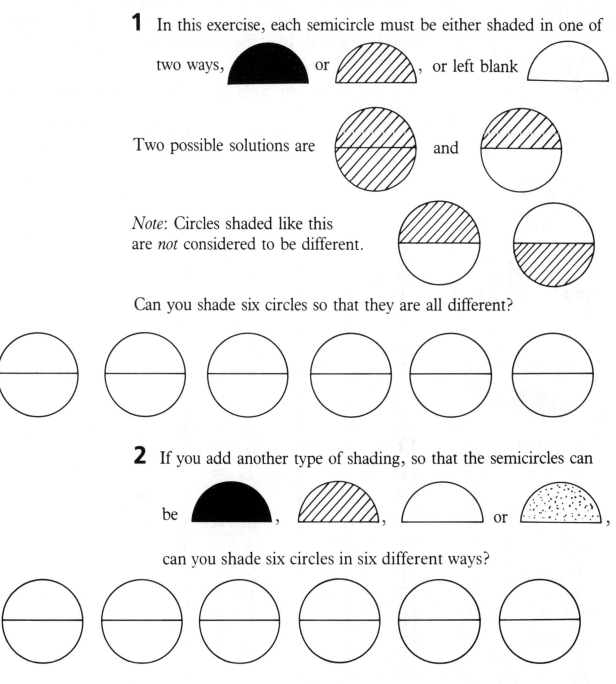

Two possible solutions are and

Note: Circles shaded like this are *not* considered to be different.

Can you shade six circles so that they are all different?

2 If you add another type of shading, so that the semicircles can be , , or ,

can you shade six circles in six different ways?

How many more ways can you find? Draw them all.

Puzzles with matches

You can make two squares with

eight matches:

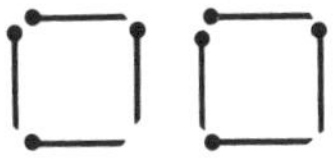

or seven matches:

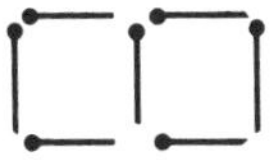

You can make three squares with

twelve matches:

or eleven matches:

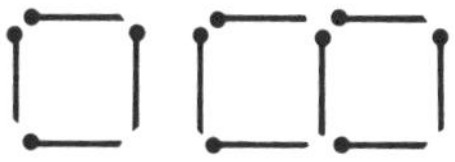

or ten matches:

Now do the following exercises.

1 Make 4 squares with:
  (a) 16 matches
  (b) 15 matches
  (c) 14 matches
  (d) 13 matches
  (e) 12 matches

2 Make 5 squares with:
  (a) 18 matches
  (b) 16 matches

3 Make 2 triangles with:
  (a) 6 matches
  (b) 5 matches

4 Make 3 triangles with:
  (a) 9 matches
  (b) 7 matches

5 Make 4 triangles with:
  (a) 12 matches
  (b) 10 matches
  (c) 9 matches

6 Look for more than one way to make 5 triangles with:
  (a) 12 matches
  (b) 11 matches.

← (DON'T PLAY WITH FIRE!)

Find my three numbers

In each question, I am thinking of three different numbers:
□, △ and ○. Using the clues given, find my three numbers.
(Guess and check is a helpful strategy.)

1
$$\triangle + \triangle = 6$$
$$\triangle + \bigcirc = \square$$
$$\square + \bigcirc = 7$$
$$\square + \square = 10$$

2
$$\triangle + \triangle = 8$$
$$\triangle + \triangle + \triangle = \bigcirc + \bigcirc$$
$$\square + \square = \bigcirc$$

3
$$\triangle + \triangle = 14$$
$$\triangle - \bigcirc = 2$$
$$\triangle - \square = 4$$
$$\bigcirc + \triangle + \square = 15$$

4
$$\square + \square = 12$$
$$\triangle - \square = \bigcirc$$
$$\bigcirc + \bigcirc + \bigcirc = \square$$
$$\triangle + \bigcirc = 10$$

5
$$\triangle + \triangle + \triangle = 12$$
$$\triangle - \square = 1$$
$$\square + \square + \square = \bigcirc$$
$$\bigcirc + \triangle = 13$$

6
$$\triangle + \square = 8$$
$$\square + \bigcirc = 16$$
$$\triangle + \bigcirc = 12$$
$$\triangle + \triangle + \triangle + \triangle = 8$$

7
$$\triangle + \triangle = 12$$
$$\triangle + \bigcirc = \square$$
$$\triangle - \bigcirc = 1$$
$$\bigcirc + \bigcirc + \bigcirc = 15$$

8
$$\triangle + \triangle = 18$$
$$\triangle - \square = 5$$
$$\bigcirc - \triangle = 3$$
$$\bigcirc - \square = 8$$

9
$$\bigcirc + \bigcirc + \bigcirc = 9$$
$$\square + \bigcirc = 10$$
$$\triangle - \square = 6$$
$$\triangle - \bigcirc = 10$$

10
$$\square + \square + \square = 18$$
$$\triangle + \triangle = 22$$
$$\triangle - \square = 5$$
$$\bigcirc - \square = 2$$

Think of three numbers of your own and make up a question
like these for others to try.

Grid puzzles

1 In each grid, draw the missing shapes and letters in such a way that every row and every column contains exactly one of each shape.

(a)

A		C
		B
B		

(b)

A	B	D	
	A		D
	C	A	
C			A

(c)

★		○	□
		★	△
	○	△	
	★		○

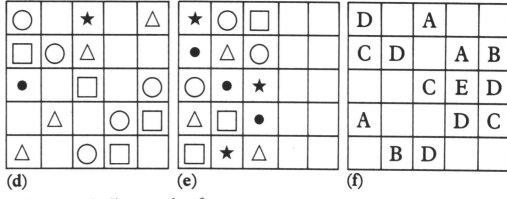

(d) (e) (f)

Make up a similar puzzle of your own.

2 Divide each of these grids into four parts so that each part contains one example of every shape. In both grids, one part has been marked for you.

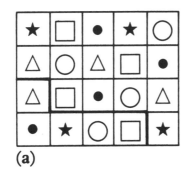

(a)

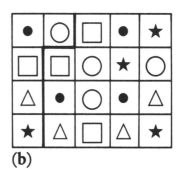

(b)

3 Divide this square into 5 separate pieces. Each piece must have one example of every shape in it. One piece has been marked for you.

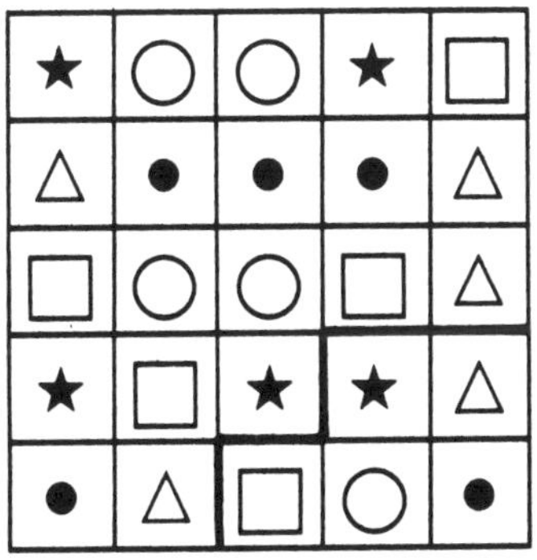

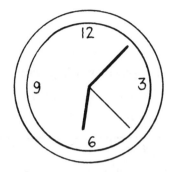

Time puzzles

1 If today is Monday, what day of the week will it be:
(a) 14 days from now?
(b) 28 days from now?
(c) 35 days from now?
(d) 37 days from now?

HOW MANY SECONDS IN A DAY?

2 If two days ago it was Wednesday, what day of the week will it be:
(a) 7 days from today?
(b) 9 days from today?
(c) 21 days from today?
(d) 20 days from today?
(e) 70 days from today?

3 How many minutes are there in:
(a) $1\frac{1}{2}$ hours?
(b) $1\frac{3}{4}$ hours?
(c) $3\frac{1}{4}$ hours?

4 When Daniel wakes up, the clock is showing 7.05. It takes him:
(a) 12 minutes to get dressed;
(b) 9 minutes to eat his breakfast;
(c) 6 minutes to clean his room;
(d) 25 minutes to practise his clarinet; and
(e) 20 minutes to travel to school.
What was the time at the end of each activity?
   Daniel was supposed to be at school by 8.30 for choir practice. How much time did he have before the practice started?

5 Claudine's birthday is on September 6. What will the date be:
(a) 25 days after her birthday?
(b) 35 days after her birthday?
(c) 60 days after her birthday?

Grid patterns

1 In the grids below, combine the figures drawn in the columns labelled A, B, C . . . with the figures drawn in the rows labelled 1, 2, 3 . . . The first two combinations have been completed for you.

(a) 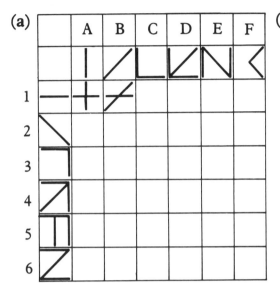 **(b)**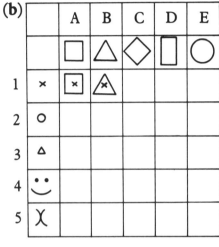

2 By working out the pattern in each matrix, complete these grids. Some of the shapes have been filled in for you.

(a) 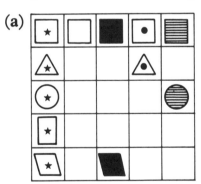 **(b)**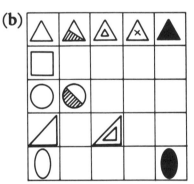

(c) 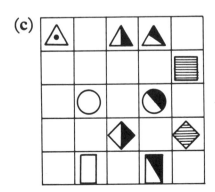 **(d)** 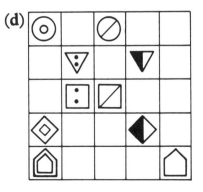 **(e)**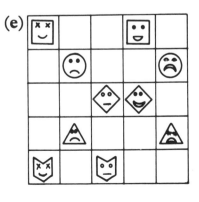

What's the value?

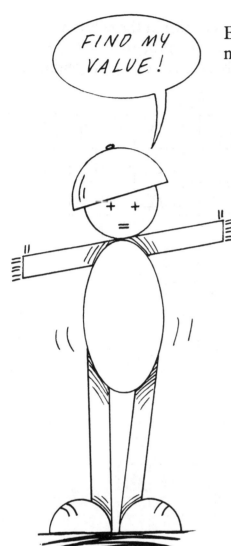

FIND MY VALUE!

Each shape used in all these sentences stands for one of the numbers from 0 to 9. Can you find the value of each one?

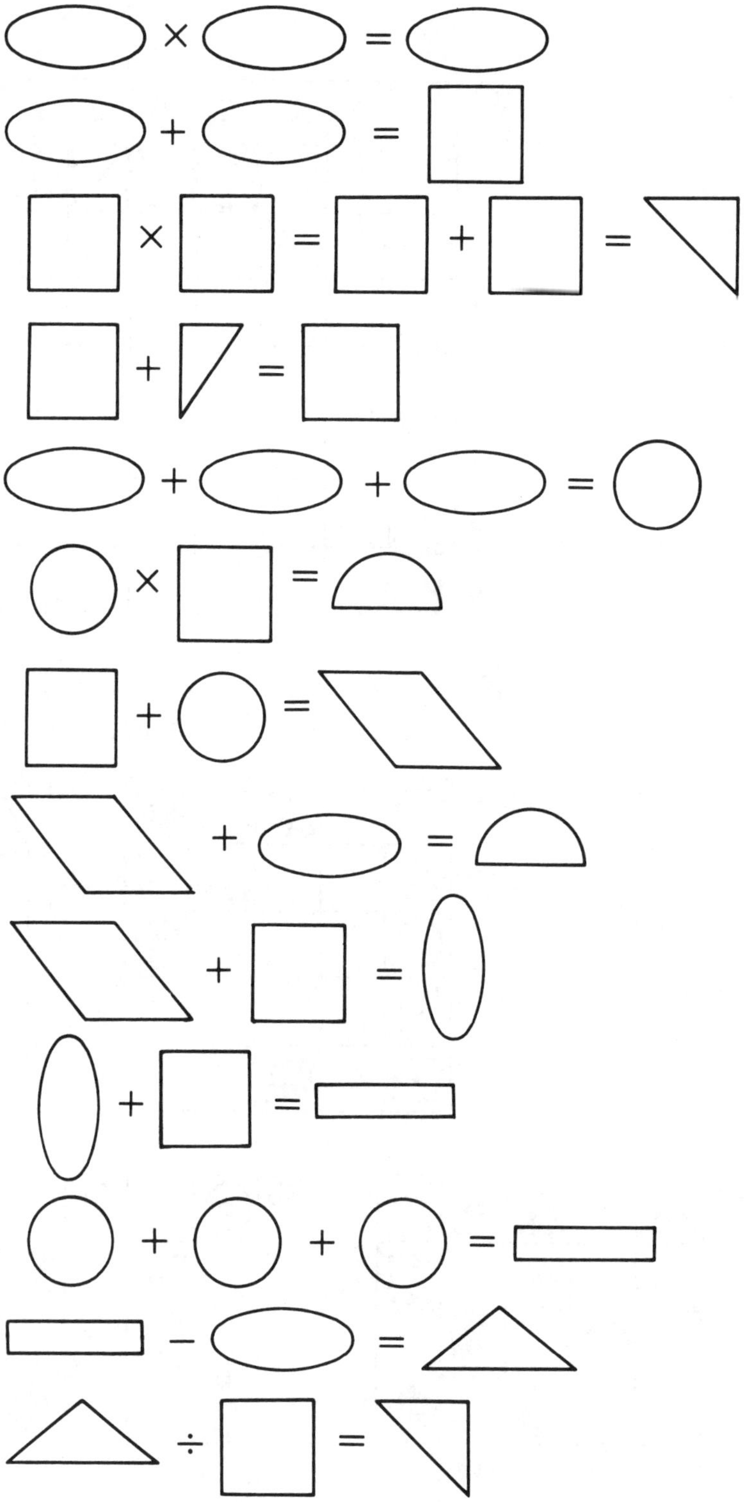

⬭ × ⬭ = ⬭

⬭ + ⬭ = ☐

☐ × ☐ = ☐ + ☐ = ◸

☐ + ◹ = ☐

⬭ + ⬭ + ⬭ = ◯

◯ × ☐ = ◠

☐ + ◯ = ▱

▱ + ⬭ = ◠

▱ + ☐ = ⬯

⬯ + ☐ = ▭

◯ + ◯ + ◯ = ▭

▭ − ⬭ = △

△ ÷ ☐ = ◿

Make up a sentence of shapes of your own.

How many routes?

WHAT A LOT OF ROOTS!

1 Amelia lives at point A. Her school, four blocks away, is at S. She can use six different short routes to walk the four blocks to school. Show each possible route on the figures below.

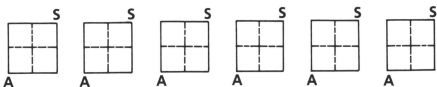

2 Raymond lives at point R. His school is five blocks away, at S. He can use ten different routes to walk the five blocks to school. One of the possible routes is drawn for you; can you show another nine ways? Are there any more?

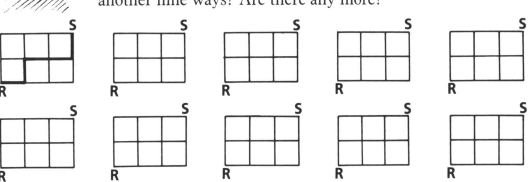

3 Visitors to Karen's flower garden must start at IN and leave at OUT. One way to write down the routes they take is to use the first letter of each flower name (C for carnation of G for gladiolus).

  (a) When a visitor wants to see the carnations, what is the shortest route to take if each flowerbed may only be passed once?

  (b) Write down all the routes visitors can take if they visit every flowerbed once and they all go first to the gladioli. One possible route could start like this:
    IN → G → P → D → and so on.

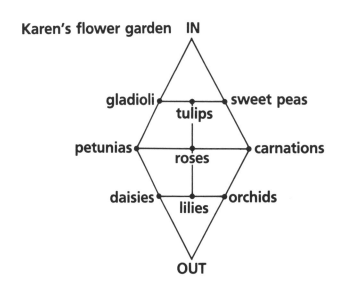

Karen's flower garden

What is my question?

1 Place digits in these squares so that the sums of the numbers are those given.

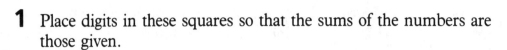

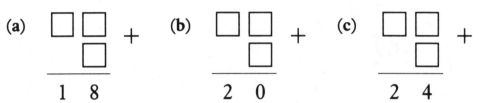

(a) □□ +
(b) □□ +
(c) □□ +

   1 8   2 0   2 4

How many solutions can you find for (a), (b) and (c)?

In exercises 2 and 3 you may not repeat the digits.

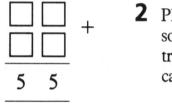

2 Place the digits 1, 2, 3 and 4 in these squares so that the sum of the numbers is 55. Now try to do this another way. How many solutions can you find?

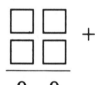

3 Place the digits 3, 4, 5 and 6 in these squares so that the sum of the numbers is 99. How many solutions can you find?

In exercise 4, you *may* repeat digits.

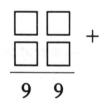

4 Place any of the digits from 1 to 8 in these squares so that the sum of the numbers is 99. One possible solution is $\frac{11}{88} +$.

$$\frac{11}{88}$$
$$\overline{99}$$

There are 64 solutions to this problem. How many can you find? Remember to work systematically.

What ? is ? my ? question ?

Triangular numbers   1

1, 3, 6 and 10 are called 'triangular numbers'. They are the numbers you get by adding the rows of dots in the triangles.

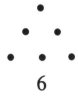

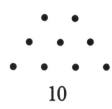

1   3   6   10

1 Continuing the pattern of dots shown above, write down the next five triangular numbers.

2 Can you see a pattern in the differences when you take away one triangular number from the one above it?

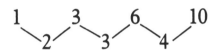

Try to use the pattern in the differences, to find the next seven triangular numbers.

3 Whenever the Friendly Society meets, the members all shake hands. How many handshakes are exchanged at the various gatherings? A table like this one may be helpful.

What patterns can you see?

Members present	Handshakes
2	1
3	3
4	
5	
6	
7	
8	

4 If 21 handshakes are exchanged, how many members are at the meeting?

5 If 55 handshakes are exchanged, how many members are at the meeting?

Triangular numbers   2

1 In each diagram, how many lines are needed to join each point to every other point? Make sure you count the lines *as you join each pair of points.*

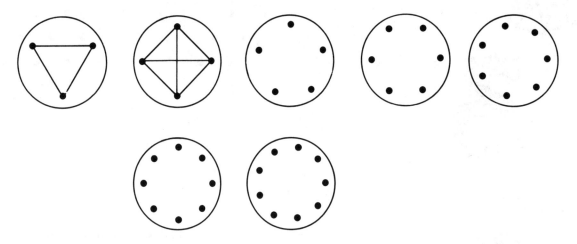

What patterns do you see?
A table like this may be helpful.

Number of points	Number of lines
3	3
4	6
5	
6	
7	
8	
9	

2 In a netball competition there are six teams. Each team plays one match against every other team.
  (a) How many matches does each team play?
  (b) How many matches are played altogether? You could use dots for the teams, as shown here.

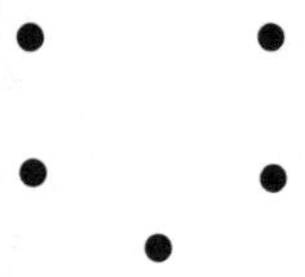

How many triangles?

A triangle has been repeatedly folded through one of its vertices, or corners.

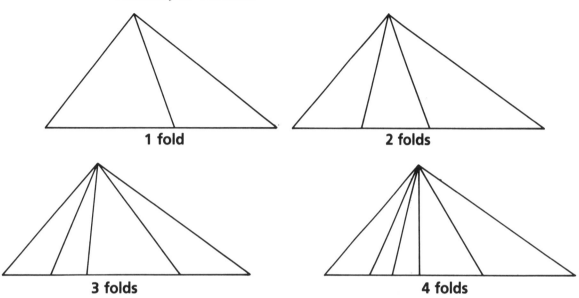

1 fold **2 folds**

3 folds **4 folds**

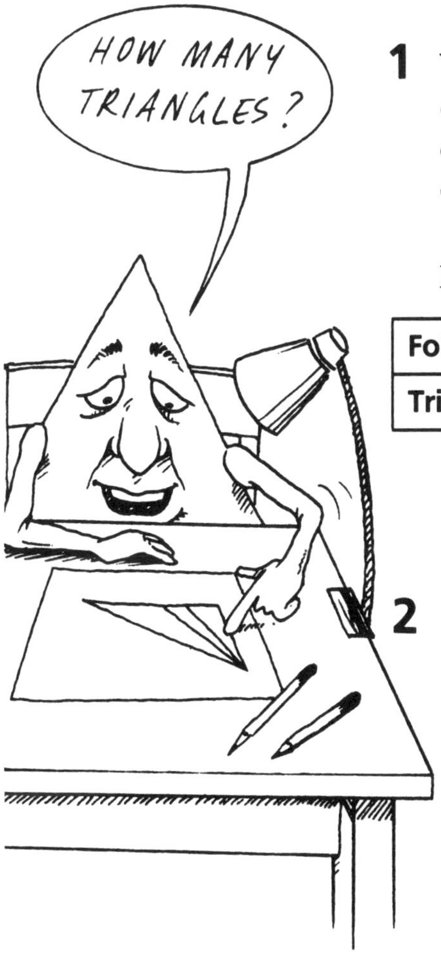

1 What is the total number of triangles formed? Remember to count the triangles systematically in each case: first, single; then double, then triple, then more than three, as needed in each case.

Completing this table may help you to discover the number pattern.

Folds	0	1	2	3	4	5
Triangles (total)	1	3				

Note that with one fold, the result is three triangles — two small and one double triangle.

2 Can you predict the number of triangles there will be after 8 folds?

Numbers in the past

1 Babylonian cuneiform (wedge writing) numerals consisted of two symbols only:

Y for 1

< for 10

12 was written like this: < Y Y
24 was written like this: < < Y Y Y Y
31 was written like this: < < < Y

(a) What do the following symbols represent in our number system?

(i)  Y Y Y   (iv)  < < < Y Y Y

(ii)  < <   (v) < Y Y Y Y Y

(iii)  < Y

(b) Write the following numbers in Babylonian cuneiform script.

(i) 4   (iv) 30

(ii) 13   (v) 45

(iii) 26

2 Mayan people used dots and strokes to represent numbers up to twenty.

This was 3: • • •

This was 5: —

This was 18:  (5 + 5 + 5 + 3)

This was 9:  (5 + 4)

(a) What do the following symbols represent in our number system?

(i) • • • •   (iv)  ≡

(ii) •   (v)

(iii)

(b) Write the following numbers as Mayan numerals.

(i) 2   (iv) 11

(ii) 7   (v) 16

(iii) 9

3 Write down your age in Babylonian cuneiform and in Mayan numerals.

Patterns and sequences

A sequence is a group of numbers that follows a pattern.
   In each group below, find the pattern, say it aloud in words and write down the next three numbers in the sequence.

1   2, 4, 6, 8

2   3, 5, 7, 9

3   7, 11, 15, 19

4   2, 9, 16, 23

5   10, 20, 30, 40

6   5, 10, 15, 20

7   11, 14, 17, 20

8   5, 15, 25, 35

9   1, 9, 17, 25

10   21, 23, 25, 27

11   30, 25, 20, 15

12   50, 48, 46, 44

13   90, 80, 70, 60

14   23, 20, 17, 14

15   42, 38, 34, 30

16   48, 43, 38, 33

17   4, 8, 12, 16

18   7, 14, 21, 28

19   18, 16, 14, 12

20   12, 23, 34, 45

21   3, 6, 9, 12

22   6, 12, 18, 24

23   1, 2, 4, 8

24   1, 2, 4, 7, 11

25   6, 9, 8, 11, 10, 13, 12

26   2, 10, 4, 20, 6, 30, 8, 40

27   1, 9, 3, 9, 5, 9, 7, 9

28   2, 5, 4, 10, 6, 15, 8, 20

29   30, 29, 27, 24

30   Make up some sequences of your own.

TRY LOOKING AT THE DIFFERENCES BETWEEN THE TWO NUMBERS LIKE I DID.

PATTERN   1   2   4   7
DIFFERENCES   1   2   3   ?

Number patterns

Find the missing number in each sequence. Say out loud what patterns you see in each sequence.

1   3, 6, ___, 12, 15, 18

2   1, 8, 11, 18, ___, 28, 31

3   2, 2, 4, 4, ___, 6, 8, 8

4   24, 21, ___, 15, 12

5   65, 60, 55, ___, 45, 40, 35, 30

6   20, ___, 21, 15, 22, 14, 23, 13

7   45, 50, 40, ___, 35, 70, 30, 80

8   2, 1, 3, 2, 4, 3, ___, 4, 6

9   12, 23, ___, 45, 56

10 45, 36, 28, 21, ___, 10, 6

11 65, 67, 70, ___, 79, 85

12 97, 93, ___, 85, 81

13 97, 96, 94, ___, 87, 82

14 97, 95, 87, 90, ___, 85, 67, 80

15 21, 25, 29, ___, 37

16 3, 9, 7, 13, 11, 17, 15, ___, 19, 25

17 $\frac{1}{4}$, $\frac{1}{2}$, 1, 2, 4, ___, 16, 32

18 1, 2, 5, 10, 11, 14, ___, 20, 23, 28

19 8, 2, 7, 3, 6, ___, 5, 5, 4

20 1, 2, 3, 6, 7, 14, 15, 30, ___, 62

21 9, 18, 10, 20, 12, 24, ___, 32, 24

22 3, 10, 5, 12, ___, 14, 9, 16

23 7, 14, 6, 12, 4, 8, ___, 0

24 24, 32, 16, 24, 12, ___, 10, 18, 9

25 2, 5, 4, 10, 6, 15, ___, 20, 10, 25, 12

26 15, 8, 16, ___, 18, 11, 22, 15, 30

27 4, 9, 16, ___, 36, 49

28 28, ___, 29, 35, 30, 34, 31, 33

29 73, 1, 64, 2, 55, 4, ___, 8

30 39, 7, 34, 10, ___, 13, 24, 16

31 Make up some sequences of your own.

Logic using scales   1

In a set of scales:

If ⬜⬜ ★★★/★★★ △ , then ⬜ △ ★★★

as it will still balance if we halve the masses on both sides;

and if ⬜⬜ ⬜★★★ △ , then ⬜ △ ★★★

as we can remove a square from each side and it will still balance.

For each of these sentences, work out what must be done to find the number of stars (★) needed to balance one square (⬜). In each case, explain why it works.

1 If ⬜⬜ ★★★★ △ , then ⬜ △ ? .

2 If ⬜⬜ ★★★★/★★★★ △ , then ⬜ △ ? .

3 If ⬜⬜⬜ ★★★★★★ △ , then ⬜ △ ? .

4 If ⬜⬜⬜ ★★★★/★★★★★ △ , then ⬜ △ ? .

5 If ⬜⬜ ⬜★★ △ , then ⬜ △ ? .

6 If ⬜⬜ ⬜★★★★ △ , then ⬜ △ ? .

7 If ⬜⬜⬜ ⬜★★ △ , then ⬜ △ ? .

8 If ⬜⬜⬜ ⬜★★★★ △ , then ⬜ △ ? .

9 If ⬜★ ★★★★ △ , then ⬜ △ ? .

10 If ⬜⬜★ ⬜★★★★ △ , then ⬜ △ ? .

11 If ⬜⬜★ ★★★★/★★★★★ △ , then ⬜ △ ? .

12 If ⬜⬜★★ ★★★★/★★★★ △ , then ⬜ △ ? .

Logic using scales   2

Work out how many stars (*) are needed to balance the scales in each of these sentences. There may be more than one way of doing these. Try to explain why your method works.

Draw some scales to help in your working.

1 If   ★★★★ ⟋△⟍ ◯◯ , then ? _____ ◯◯◯ .

2 If   ★★★ ⟋△⟍ ☐◯ , then ? _____ ☐☐☐◯◯◯ .

3 If   ◯★ ⟋△⟍ ☐   and   ★★★ ⟋△⟍ ◯ , then ? _____ ☐ .

4 If   ★★☐ ⟋△⟍ ◯◯   and   ★★★ ⟋△⟍ ☐ , then ? _____ ◯◯ .

5 If   ◯◯ ⟋△⟍ ☐   and   ◯ ⟋△⟍ ★★ , then ? _____ ☐ .

6 If   ★★ over ★★★ ⟋△⟍ ☐◯   and   ★★★ ⟋△⟍ ☐ , then ? _____ ◯ .

7 If   ◯◯◯ ⟋△⟍ ☐★   and   ◯ ⟋△⟍ ★ , then ? _____ ☐ .

8 If   ◯◯◯ ⟋△⟍ ☐☐   and   ★★ ⟋△⟍ ◯ , then ? _____ ☐ .

9 If   ◯◯ ⟋△⟍ ☐☐☐   and   ★★★ ⟋△⟍ ◯ , then ? _____ ☐ .

10 If   ◯◯ ⟋△⟍ ☐☐★★   and   ☐ ⟋△⟍ ★★★ , then ? _____ ◯ .

Shading halves and quarters

1 One half of each of these shapes has been shaded.

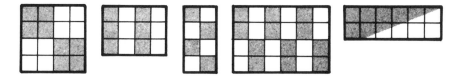

Can you shade half of each of these shapes in three different ways? If you can find more solutions, draw them on squared paper.

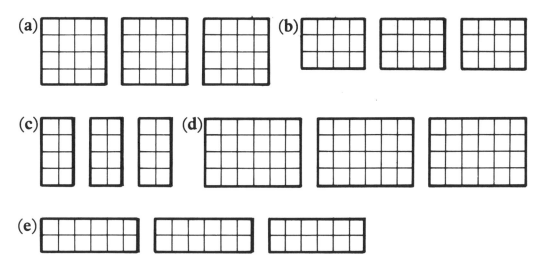

2 One-quarter of each of these shapes has been shaded.

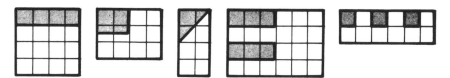

Can you shade one-quarter of each of these shapes in two different ways?

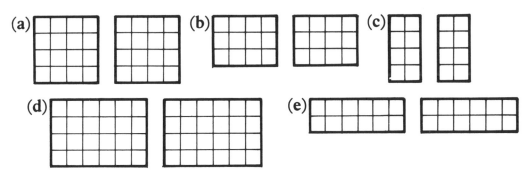

Secret codes

1 Using the code below, the word 'SECRET' would be written like this:

A	B	C
D	E	F
G	H	I

J	K	L
M	N	O
P	Q	R

S	T	U
V	W	X
Y	Z	and

(a) Can you translate this sentence?

(b) Now write 'TEACHERS HAVE CLASS', using the same code.

2 Here is a different code. Use it to work out the message below.

A	B
D	C

E	F
H	G

I	J
L	K

M	N
P	O

Q	R
T	S

U	V
X	W

Y
Z

3 Crack the code!

Each letter of the alphabet is represented by a number.

A ...   G ...   M ...   S ...   Y ...
B ...   H ...   N ...   T ...   Z ...
C ...   I ...   O ...   U ...
D ...   J ...   P ...   V ...
E ...   K ...   Q ...   W ...
F ...   L ...   R ...   X ...

DIG is written as 2 7 5.

MAT is written as 11 25 18. Can you see the pattern?

(a) Using this secret code, write these words:
- (i) CAT
- (ii) HUNGRY
- (iii) MATHS

(b) The following message was written in the same code:

6 13 14 3   23 13 19   25 16 3   3 12 8 13 23 7 12 5

18 6 7 17. Can you translate it?

Differences

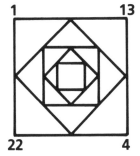

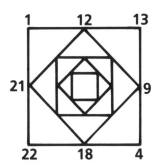

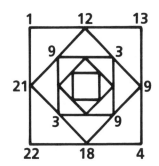

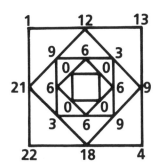

In this exercise, you start with four numbers at the corners of the large square.

In the middle of each side, you write down the difference between the two corner numbers.

Then in the middle of the smaller square, you write down the difference between the two corner numbers.

This is repeated until you have zero on all the corners. In this case, it has taken 4 steps.

Complete the differences for the squares below. You can use the grids on page 48. In each case find how many steps it takes. Try to find one of your own that takes more than 4 steps.

(a)

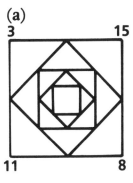

(b)

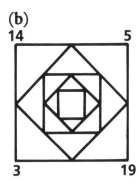

(c)

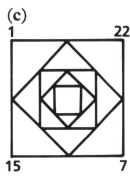

(d)

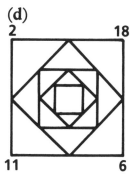

(e)

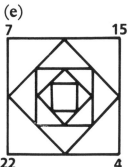

(f)

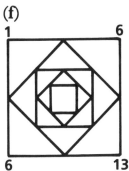

(g)

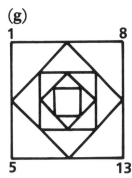

(h)

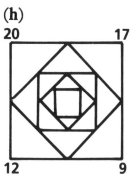

Folding paper

1 Take a sheet of paper.
Fold it in half. Unfold it and count the number of small rectangles.
Refold it, then fold it in half again.

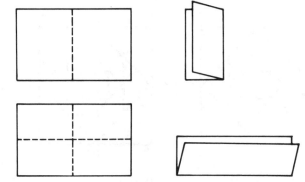

After each fold, unfold the paper and count the number of rectangles you have made. Continue doing this until the paper can no longer be folded.

(a) Complete this table.

Folds	1	2	3	4	5	6
Small rectangles	2	4				

Now experiment with paper of different sizes and thicknesses.

(b) What is the maximum number of folds you can make?

(c) Can you predict the number of small rectangles that will be made with 8 folds?

2 (a) Take a long sheet of paper, and fold it in half towards you. Refold it in half away from you, then again in half towards you, and so on until you can no longer fold the paper.

After each fold, unfold the paper and count the number of creases on it. As you work, complete this table.

Folds	1	2	3	4
Creases	1			
Rectangles	2			

(b) Can you predict the number of rectangles that will be made with 7 folds?

3 What patterns do you see in these tables? Try to find out how these numbers are used in computing.

HOORAY

Solutions

Missing shapes (page 6)

It will be helpful in these exercises if children repeat the patterns orally, as suggested in the first two solutions below.

1 ○ □ The pattern is 'square, circle, square, two circles', and then this is repeated.

2 ○ □ The pattern is 'oval, square, oval, oval, square, square', and this will be repeated.

3 ○   4 □ ○ 5 ○ ○ 6 □ ◇ 7 □ ○

8 △ □ 9 cc 10 cc 11 • \

12 Making up questions of their own helps them to make the patterns more explicit and gives the children a more open and active role.

Faces (page 7)

In these exercises it is helpful to try to work systematically.

1 It is worthwhile to discuss with the children how they intend to draw the 12 faces. If they have not previously come across problems that involved working systematically, the procedure should be discussed.

In this case it would be best to draw first all the possible faces with, say, curly hair and eyes closed, then those with curly hair and eyes open, and then all possible combinations with straight hair.

Of course, all the possible combinations with a happy mouth could equally well have been drawn first. The important thing is to work to a plan — to establish an order in which the features will be used, not to select them haphazardly. Without a systematic approach, it is extremely difficult to work out what is missing and to ensure that all possibilities have been accounted for.

2

Shapes and symbols (page 8)

It is important to draw children's attention to each aspect of the shapes and to consider both horizontal and vertical patterns.

1   2   3

4   5 ★ 6

7   8   9

Torn rectangles (page 9)

Children could complete each rectangle and then count the little squares.

1 8 **2** 12 **3** 14 **4** 15 **5** 18 **6** 9
7 20 **8** 18

Describing how they tackled the problem develops both language and ideas.

Shape puzzles (page 10)

Children can outline the shapes and count them.

1	**2**	**3**	
(a) 2	(a) 4	(a) 3	(f) 4
(b) 4	(b) 5	(b) 4	(g) 5
(c) 6	(c) 6	(c) 2	(h) 6
(d) 6	(d) 8	(d) 2	
(e) 9	(e) 3	(e) 6	
(f) 4			

Number sentences (page 11)

This exercise assumes only knowledge of 2 times table.

1 $1 + 2 - 3 = 0$ **2** $1 \times 3 - 2 = 1$ **3** $1 + 3 - 2 = 2$
4 $2 + 3 - 1 = 4$
5 $2 \times 3 - 1 = 5$ or $2 + 3 \times 1 = 5$ or $(2 + 3) \times 1 = 5$
6 $1 \times 2 \times 3 = 6$ or $1 + 2 + 3 = 6$ **7** $1 \times 3 + 4 = 7$
8 $2 + 4 - 6 = 0$ **9** $2 \times 4 - 6 = 2$ **10** $2 \times 3 - 5 = 1$
11 $2 \times 5 - 6 = 4$ **12** $2 \times 5 - 1 = 9$
13 $2 \times 4 - 3 = 5$ **14** $6 - 2 + 4 = 8$ or $6 \times 2 - 4 = 8$
15 $2 + 6 - 4 = 4$ **16** $2 \times 4 - 5 = 3$
17 $2 \times 3 + 1 = 7$ **18** $2 \times 5 + 2 = 12$
19 $2 \times 5 - 2 = 8$ **20** $2 \times 6 - 5 = 7$

Brackets have not been included in the answers above where the conventional rules apply, i.e. multiply before you add or subtract.

Shading circles (page 12)

Working systematically is essential in this exercise. It is important to discuss shading combinations with the children, deciding with them which are different and which are not.

1

2

Puzzles with matches (page 13)

Children should be provided with matches so that this can be a practical exercise.

1 (a)    (b)

(c)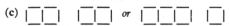

(d)    (e)

2 (a)

(b)

3 (a) 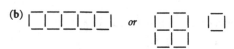   (b)

4 (a)    (b)

5 (a)

(b)

(c) or or

6 (a) or or

(b) or or other shapes

Find my three numbers (page 14)

1 2 lots of △ = 6
  ∴ △ = 3
  2 lots of □ = 10
  ∴ □ = 5
  Since △ + ○ = □
  3 + ○ = 5
  ∴ ○ = 2

2 2 lots of △ = 8
  ∴ △ = 4
  Now, 4 + 4 + 4 = ○ + ○
  ∴ 12 = ○ + ○
  ∴ ○ = 6
  and 2 lots of □ = 6
  ∴ □ = 3

3 △ = 7
  ○ = 5
  □ = 3

4 □ = 6
  ○ = 2
  △ = 8

5 △ = 4
  □ = 3
  ○ = 9

6 △ = 2
  □ = 6
  ○ = 10

7 △ = 6
  ○ = 5
  □ = 11

8 △ = 9
  □ = 4
  ○ = 12

9 △ = 13
  ○ = 3
  □ = 7

10 □ = 6
  △ = 11
  ○ = 8

Grid puzzles (page 15)

These questions require children to examine each grid very carefully. They may have to use trial-and-error with the shapes and letters.

1 (a)

A	B	C
C	A	B
B	C	A

(b)

A	B	D	C
B	A	C	D
D	C	A	B
C	D	B	A

(c)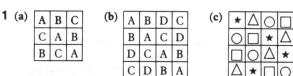

(d)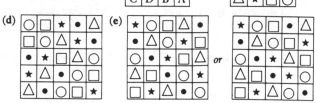

(e) or

(f)

D	C	A	B	E
C	D	E	A	B
B	A	C	E	D
A	E	B	D	C
E	B	D	C	A

2 (a) 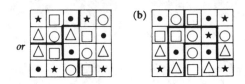 or

or

(b)

3 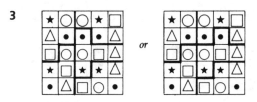 or

34

Time puzzles (page 16)

1 (a) Monday; (b) Monday; (c) Monday; (d) Wednesday

2 If two days ago it was Wednesday, today is Friday.
 (a) Friday; (b) Sunday; (c) Friday; (d) Thursday;
 (e) Friday

3 There are 60 minutes in 1 hour, 30 minutes in $\frac{1}{2}$ hour,
 15 minutes in $\frac{1}{4}$ hour, 45 minutes in $\frac{3}{4}$ hour.
 (a) 90 minutes; (b) 105 minutes; (c) 195 minutes

4 (a) dressed: 7.17
 (b) breakfast eaten: 7.26
 (c) room cleaned: 7.32
 (d) clarinet practised: 7.57
 (e) school reached: 8.17
 Daniel had 13 minutes before choir practice started.

5 There are 30 days in September and 31 days in October.
 (a) October 1; (b) October 11; (c) November 5

Grid patterns (page 17)

1 (a)

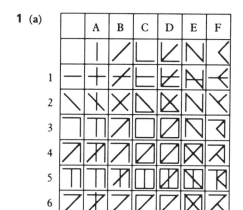

(b)

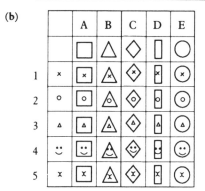

2 (a)

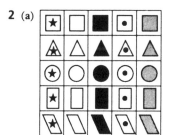

(b)

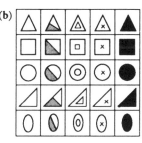

(c)

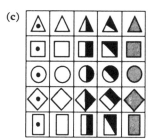

(d)

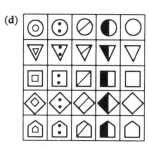

(e)

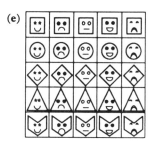

What's the value? (page 18)

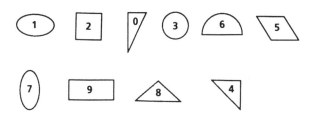

The first sentence gives a good start. For this, we need to find
a number which when multiplied by itself will remain the same.
∴ ◯ can be either 1 or 0.
Now, since 0 + 0 = 0, and in the second sentence ◯ + ◯ is
not equal to ◯, ◯ cannot be 0.
∴ ◯ = 1
From the second sentence, ▢ = 2; from the third sentence,
◺ = 4; and from the fifth sentence, ◯ = 3.
Children can continue to use the accumulated information to
find the value of the other shapes.
 Making up one for themselves helps to reinforce the ideas.

How many routes? (page 19)

Children need to work systematically when doing these
questions. They can adopt a system such as 'First mark all
routes that move up (or go north)', although that may not
necessarily be the choice.

1

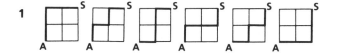

2

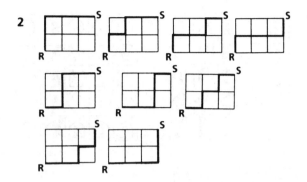

3 (a) IN → S → C → O → OUT
  (b) IN → G → P → D → L → R → T → S → C → O → OUT
  IN → G → P → R → T → S → C → O → L → D → OUT
  IN → G → T → S → C → R → P → D → L → O → OUT
  IN → G → T → S → C → O → L → R → P → D → OUT

What is my question? (page 20)

These questions are excellent in testing and reinforcing addition facts. Systematic work is helpful in listing all possible solutions. Children may need to discuss the layout of the questions. They should be encouraged to use their own layout. e.g.

10
or 10 + 8 = 18   + 8
────
18

1 (a)
$$\frac{10}{8}=18 \quad \frac{11}{7}=18 \quad \frac{12}{6}=18 \quad \frac{13}{5}=18 \quad \frac{14}{4}=18 \quad \frac{15}{3}=18 \quad \frac{16}{2}=18 \quad \frac{17}{1}=18$$

(b)
$$\frac{11}{9}=20 \quad \frac{12}{8}=20 \quad \frac{13}{7}=20 \quad \frac{14}{6}=20 \quad \frac{15}{5}=20 \quad \frac{16}{4}=20 \quad \frac{17}{3}=20 \quad \frac{18}{2}=20$$
$$\frac{19}{1}=20$$

(c)
$$\frac{20}{4}=24 \quad \frac{21}{3}=24 \quad \frac{22}{2}=24 \quad \frac{23}{1}=24 \quad \frac{19}{5}=24 \quad \frac{18}{6}=24 \quad \frac{17}{7}=24 \quad \frac{16}{8}=24$$
$$\frac{15}{9}=24$$

and reversing rows:

2
$$\frac{34}{21}=55 \quad \frac{31}{24}=55 \quad \frac{43}{12}=55 \quad \frac{13}{42}=55 \quad \frac{21}{34}=55 \quad \frac{24}{31}=55 \quad \frac{12}{43}=55 \quad \frac{42}{13}=55$$

3
$$\frac{65}{34}=99 \quad \frac{64}{35}=99 \quad \frac{56}{43}=99 \quad \frac{46}{53}=99 \quad \frac{34}{65}=99 \quad \frac{35}{64}=99 \quad \frac{43}{56}=99 \quad \frac{53}{46}=99$$

4 Examples (shaded)

$$\frac{11}{88} + \frac{12}{87} +$$
$$\overline{99} \quad \overline{99}$$

		Second 2 digits							
		1	2	3	4	5	6	7	8
		8	7	6	5	4	3	2	1
First 2 digits	1	11	12	13	14	15	16	17	18
	8	88	87	86	85	84	83	82	81
	2	21	22	23	24	25	26	27	28
	7	78	77	76	75	74	73	72	71
	3	31	32	33	34	35	36	37	38
	6	68	67	66	65	64	63	62	61
	4	41	42	43	44	45	46	47	48
	5	58	57	56	55	54	53	52	51
	5	51	52	53	54	55	56	57	58
	4	48	47	46	45	44	43	42	41
	6	61	62	63	64	65	66	67	68
	3	38	37	36	35	34	33	32	31
	7	71	72	73	74	75	76	77	78
	2	28	27	26	25	24	23	22	21
	8	81	82	83	84	85	86	87	88
	1	18	17	16	15	14	13	12	11

These solutions are expressed in table form for your convenience. Children are not likely to write their answers like this.

Triangular numbers 1 (page 21)

1   15   21   28

36   45

Children could also build these towers using centicubes. Discuss with them the fact that as the towers grow, the base layers increase by one extra number each time. This is the reason for the pattern of differences shown in question 2.

2
1 —2— 3 —3— 6 —4— 10 —5— 15 —6— 21 —7— 28 —8— 36 —9—

45 —10— 55 —11— 66

3 An experiment should be done with children shaking hands with family or friends. They really enjoy it, and get quite a thrill when they discover that the resulting numbers follow the pattern (above) of triangular numbers.

Members present	Handshakes
2	1
3	3
4	6
5	10
6	15
7	21
8	28
9	36
10	45
11	55

4 7 members

5 11 members (answered by continuing the table).

Triangular numbers 2 (page 22)

1

Number of points	Number of lines
3	3
4	6
5	10
6	15
7	21
8	28
9	36

2 (a) 5
  (b) 15

Discuss the similarity of this question to the one above. As an extension, children could be asked to make up their own questions, the answers to which will use the triangular numbers; for example: 'A family of six all buy presents for each other. How many presents are bought altogether?'

In this case, discuss families of three, four and five first. The results will equal twice the triangular numbers — that is, 6, 12, 20 and 30.

How many triangles? (page 23)

1

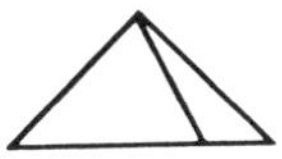

1 fold

Single triangles 2
Double triangles 1
Total 3

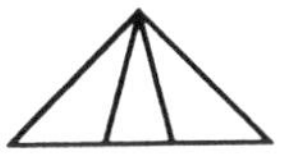

2 folds

Single triangles 3
Double triangles 2
Triple triangles 1
Total 6

3 folds

Single triangles 4
Double triangles 3 ⎫
Triple triangles 2 ⎬ Note the pattern here.
Large triangle 1 ⎭
Total 10

The shading in the figure below covers a double triangle.

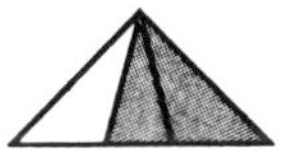

When counting the total number of triangles, children should be encouraged to set out their work in their own way. One possible way is shown above. If they have difficulty, they should be asked to draw and shade the triangles, as shown here:

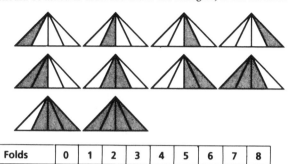

Folds	0	1	2	3	4	5	6	7	8
Triangles	1	3	6	10	15	21	28	36	45

2 It is important to note that the total numbers of triangles follow the pattern of the triangular numbers. Children should find this result fascinating.

Completing the pattern (as above), we can easily show that the number of triangles for 8 folds is 45.

Numbers in the past (page 24)

1 (a) (i) 3
     (ii) 20
     (iii) 11
     (iv) 33
     (v) 15

  (b) (i) VVVV
     (ii) <VVV
     (iii) <<VVVVVV
     (iv) <<<
     (v) <<<<VVVVV

2 (a) (i) 4
     (ii) 6
     (iii) 12
     (iv) 15
     (v) 19

  (b) (i) ••
     (ii) ••
     (iii) ••••
     (iv) •
     (v) •

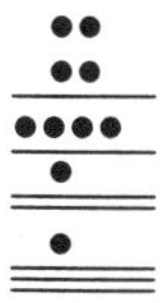

Patterns and sequences (page 25)

		Pattern
1	10, 12, 14	+2 (add 2)
2	11, 13, 15	+2
3	23, 27, 31	+4
4	30, 37, 44	+7
5	50, 60, 70	+10
6	25, 30, 35	+5
7	23, 26, 29	+3
8	45, 55, 65	+10
9	33, 41, 49	+8
10	29, 31, 33	+2
11	10, 5, 0	−5 (subtract 5)
12	42, 40, 38	−2
13	50, 40, 30	−10
14	11, 8, 5	−3
15	26, 22, 18	−4

16	28, 23, 18	−5
17	20, 24, 28	+4
18	35, 42, 49	+7
19	10, 8, 6	−2
20	56, 67, 78	+11
21	15, 18, 21	+3
22	30, 36, 42	+6
23	16, 32, 64	×2 (double), times 2
24	16, 22, 29	+1, +2, +3, +4, +5 + 6, +7
25	15, 14, 17	2 patterns: 6, 8, 10, 12, 14 and 9, 11, 13, 15, 17
26	10, 50, 12	2 patterns: 2, 4, 6, 8, 10, 12 and 10, 20, 30, 40, 50
27	9, 9, 11	2 patterns: 1, 3, 5, 7, 9, 11, and 9 between each number
28	10, 25, 12	2 patterns: 2, 4, 6, 8, 10, 12 and 5, 10, 15, 20, 25
29	20, 15, 9	−1, −2, −3, −4, −5, −6

Number patterns (page 26)

Children should be encouraged to express the patterns in their own words. However, in the solutions below the symbols + (for add) and − (for subtract) have been used.

		Pattern
1	9	+3
2	21	+7, +3; or 2 patterns: 1, 11, <u>21</u>, 31 and 8, 18, 28
3	6	repeat number, then +2
4	18	−3
5	50	−5
6	16	2 patterns: 20, 21, 22, 23 and <u>16</u>, 15, 14, 13
7	60	2 patterns: 45, 40, 35, 30 and <u>50</u>, 60, 70, 80
8	5	2 patterns: 2, 3, 4, <u>5</u>, 6 and 1, 2, <u>3</u>, 4
9	34	+11
10	15	−9, −8, −7, −6, −5, −4; or triangular numbers in reverse
11	74	+2, +3, +4, +5, +6
12	89	−4
13	91	−1, −2, −3, −4, −5
14	77	2 patterns: 97, 87, <u>77</u>, 67 and 95, 90, 85, 80
15	33	+4
16	21	+6, then −2; or 2 patterns: 3, 7, 11, 15, 19 and 9, 13, 17, <u>21</u>, 25
17	8	double (or ×2)
18	19	+1, then +3, then +5
19	4	2 patterns: 8, 7, 6, 5, 4 and 2, 3, <u>4</u>, 5
20	31	double (or ×2), then +1
21	16	double (or ×2), then −8
22	7	+7, then −5; or 2 patterns: 3, 5, <u>7</u>, 9 and 10, 12, 14, 16
23	0	double (or ×2), then −8
24	20	+8, then halve (or ÷2)
25	8	2 patterns: 2, 4, 6, <u>8</u>, 10, 12 and 5, 10, 15, 20, 25
26	9	−7, then double
27	25	square numbers; or +5, +7, +9, +11, +13
28	36	2 patterns: 28, 29, 30, 31 and <u>36</u>, 35, 34, 33
29	46	2 patterns: 73, 64, 55, <u>46</u> (−9) and 1, 2, 4, 8
30	29	2 patterns: 39, 34, <u>29</u>, <u>24</u> (−5) and 7, 10, 13, 16

Logic using scales 1 (page 27)

It would be helpful if children could do some experiments with a set of scales before tackling these exercises. A discussion of the examples will help some of them. It will also help to get them to talk about the ways they solve the problems.

1★★ Halve each side.
2★★★★ Halve each side.
3★★ Find one-third of each side.
4★★★ Find one-third of each side.
5★★ Remove one □ from each side.
6★★★★★ Remove one □ from each side.
7★ Remove one □ from each side, then halve.
8★★ Remove one □ from each side, then halve.
9★★★ Remove one ★ from each side.
10★★★★ Remove one □ and one ★ from each side.
11★★★★ Remove one ★ from each side, then halve.
12★★★ Remove two ★'s from each side, then halve.

Logic using scales 2 (page 28)

Children will need help talking through these problems.

1 ★★★★★★ Use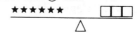

2 ★★★★★★★★ Triple first scale.
3 ★★★★ Replace ○ with ★★★ on first scale.
4 ★★★★★ Replace □ with ★★★ on first scale.
5 ★★★★ Replace each ○ with ★★ on first scale.
6 ★★ Replace □ with ★★★ on first scale.

Now remove ★★★ from both sides.
7 ★★ Replace each ○ with ★ on first scale:

★★★   □★

Now remove ★ from both sides.
8 ★★★ Replace each ○ with ★★ on first scale:
★★★★★★   □□

Now, since two □s balance six ★s, one □ balances three ★s.
9★★ Replace each ○ with ★★★:
★★★★★★   □□□

Now, since three □s balance six ★s, one □ balances two ★s.
10 ★★★★ Replace each □ with ★★★:
       ★★★
○○   ★★★★★

Now, since two ○'s balance eight ★s, one ○ balances four ★s.

38

Shading halves and quarters (page 29)

Some possible solutions are drawn below. All the shadings can be done in reverse, so that the white parts can be shaded and the shaded parts left white. Also, all the shapes can be turned. Children can turn this book 90°, so that ▯ is the same as ▭ in the first question.

1 Please remember that there are many more possible solutions.

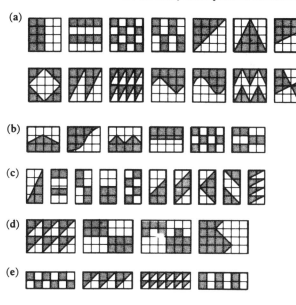

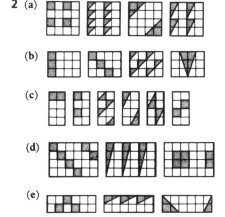

Secret codes (page 30)

1 (a) HOLIDAYS ARE FUN

(b)

Students could make up their own secret messages.

2 THIS IS VERY HARD.

3

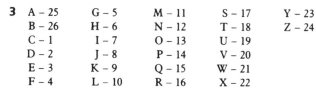

A – 25	G – 5	M – 11	S – 17	Y – 23
B – 26	H – 6	N – 12	T – 18	Z – 24
C – 1	I – 7	O – 13	U – 19	
D – 2	J – 8	P – 14	V – 20	
E – 3	K – 9	Q – 15	W – 21	
F – 4	L – 10	R – 16	X – 22	

(a) (i) 1 25 18
(ii) 6 19 12 5 16 23
(iii) 11 25 18 6 17

(b) HOPE YOU ARE ENJOYING THIS.

Differences (page 31)

With this puzzle, children can be happily subtracting for hours. They should notice that the square before the final one will have four identical numbers at the vertices.

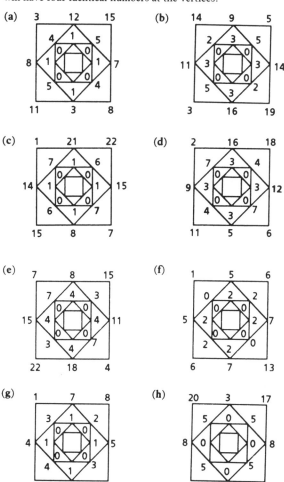

Children can make up their own questions, using copies of the grid paper on page 48. They will have to choose their own corner numbers.

Note that some groups of corner numbers will give sequences that are longer than 4 steps

Folding paper (page 32)

It is worthwhile having a discussion with the children before starting this experiment. They should first be asked how many times they think a sheet of paper can be folded in half, and then experiment with paper of different sizes and thicknesses.

They usually find the results amazing.

1 (a)

Folds	1	2	3	4	5	6	7	8
Rectangles	2	4	8	16	32	64	128	256

Continue the pattern to predict the results of 7 and 8 folds.

(b) The maximum number of times that a sheet of paper can be folded is 8; however, depending on the size and thickness of the paper, it may be possible to fold it only 6 or 7 times.

(c) 256

2 (a)

Folds	1	2	3	4	5	6	7
Creases	1	3	7	15	31	63	127
Rectangles	2	4	8	16	32	64	128

Continue the pattern to predict the results of 5, 6 and 7 folds.

Again, depending on the size and thickness of the paper, it may be possible to fold it only 4 times.

(b) 128

3 They are called powers of 2. They are used a lot in computing for example in the names of computers or in the size of computer memories.

e.g. $1024 = 2^{10}$ is called 1K

Grid paper and diagram masters

6 mm square paper

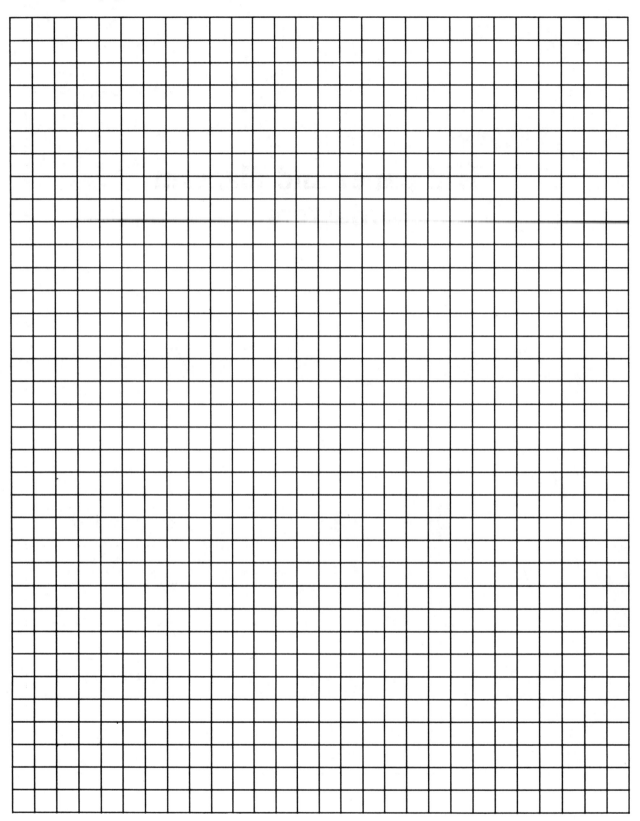

1 cm square paper

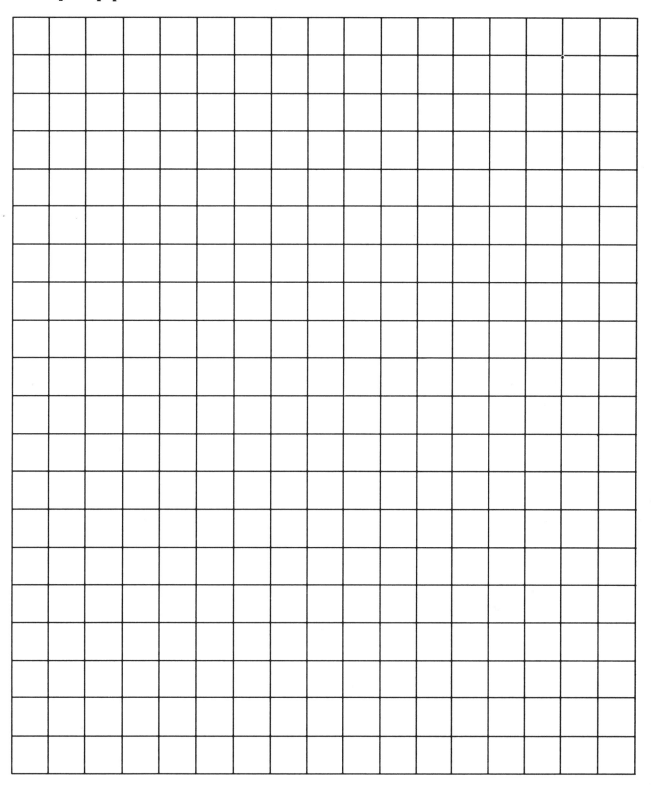

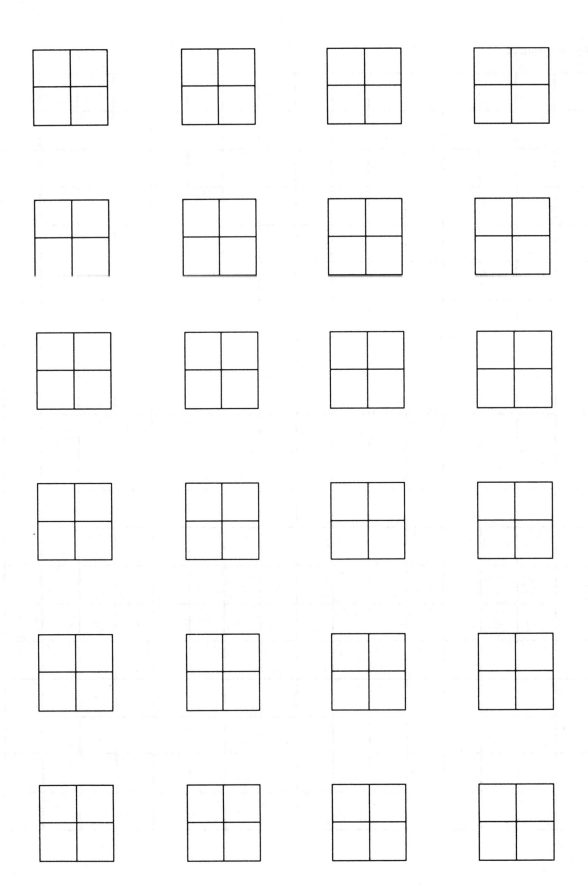

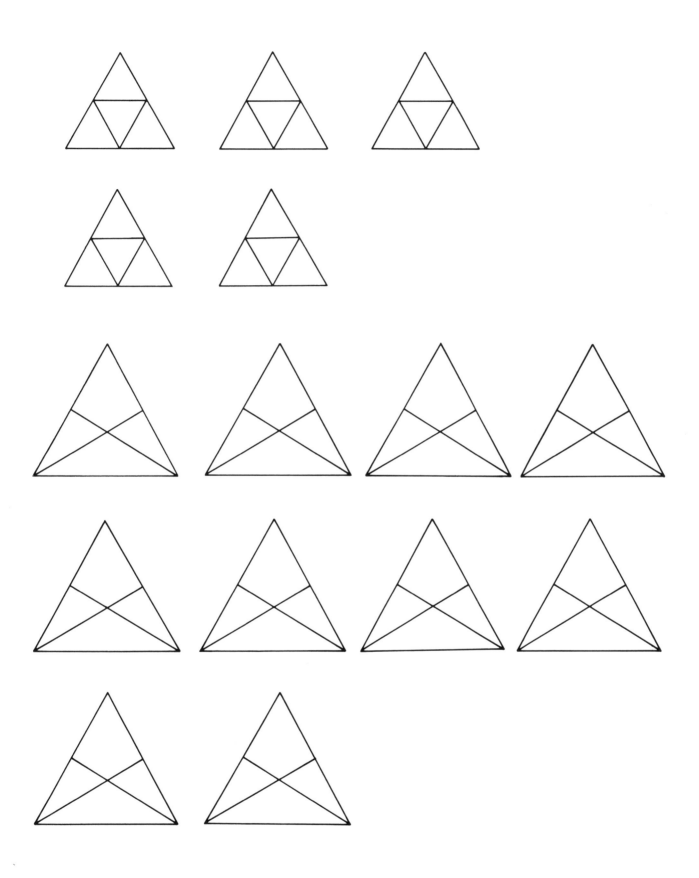

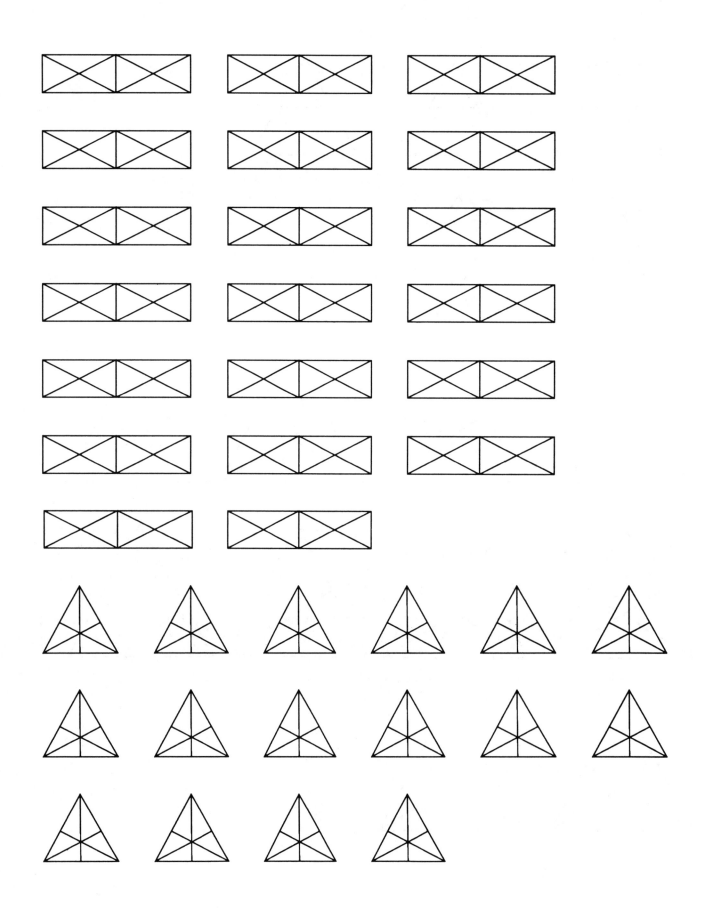

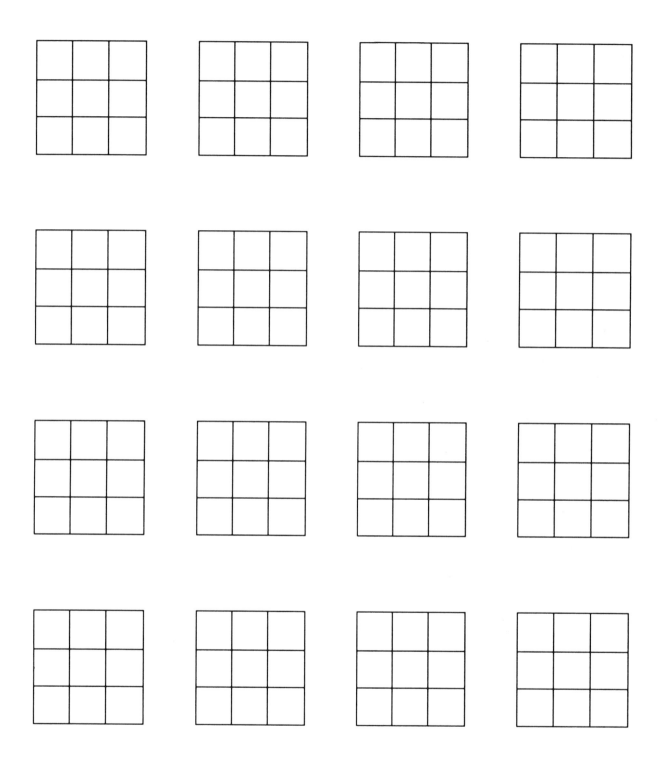

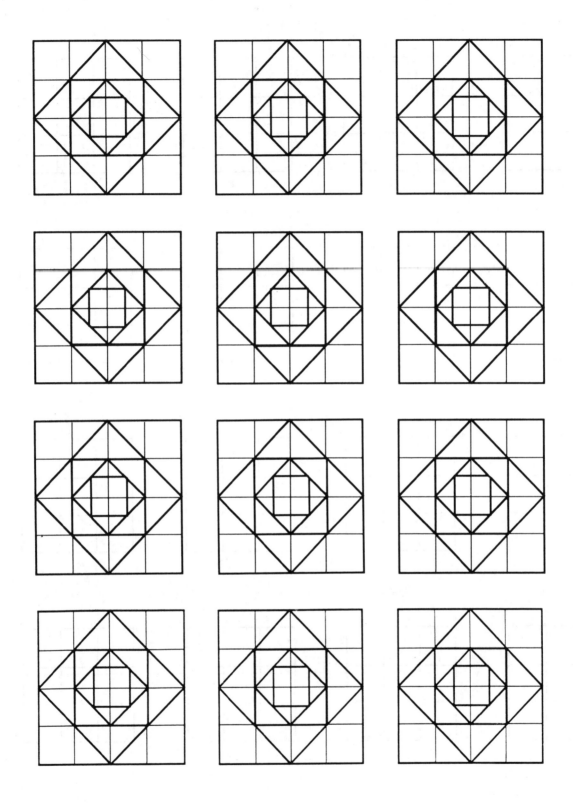